Curator's welcome

It is my pleasure to welcome you, on behalf of all the staff who are privileged to work here at the Royal Botanic Garden Edinburgh (RBGE). We hope that you will enjoy your time here – whether you are a regular visitor to the Garden or in Edinburgh for the first time.

RBGE started in 1670 as a medicinal plant or physic garden to cultivate, study and – perhaps more importantly – ensure that the plants used in medicine at that time were accurately named. As the number of plants cultivated increased, and therefore the space required to cultivate increased, so the Garden moved several times within Edinburgh until in 1820 it arrived at this site in Inverleith. It was not until 1876, with the final purchase of land surrounding Inverleith House, that the Garden as we know it today was complete.

We are fortunate here in Edinburgh to have a reasonably benign climate that allows the cultivation of a wide range of plants outdoors and an extensive collection under glass. The horticulture team further manipulates the many different aspects and microclimates throughout the Garden and in the Glasshouses to maximise the number of species cultivated.

Today, within the 28 ha of the Garden and Living Collection, we cultivate an astonishing range of over 13,500 plant species and over 128,000 plants from 156 countries in a diverse range of habitats that visitors can enjoy during their visit. This includes 10 distinct climatic zones in the Display Glasshouses, the Rock Garden, the Alpine House area, the Woodland Garden, the Pond area, the Arboretum or tree collection, Scottish Native Plants, one of the largest collections of Chinese plants outside China on the Chinese Hillside, and an astonishingly diverse *Rhododendron* collection.

However, the Garden landscape and plant collection that the visitor walks through and enjoys today is only one element of the important work of a modern botanic garden. In the Herbarium, RBGE has an extremely large and important reference collection of over 3 million dried plant specimens, and the equally important and significant botanical and horticultural Library and Archive. With the Living Collection, the Herbarium, the Library and the laboratories, the staff at RBGE continue our important work of exploring, conserving and explaining the world of plants for a better future.

As the population of the world increases and puts increasing pressure on the diminishing natural resources of the planet, I hope that through exploring the Garden or participating in one of our many public engagement activities you will leave with a deeper appreciation and understanding of the importance – to our all futures – of plants and their conservation.

David Knott, Curator, Royal Botanic Garden Edinburgh

Contents

What we do

The Royal Botanic Garden Edinburgh (RBGE) is one of the world's leading botanic gardens. A botanic garden is an establishment that displays, studies and teaches about plants. Visitors can discover our fascinating history dating back nearly 350 years, learn about its plants and trees through interpretation panels and public engagement events, and walk around 28 ha of beautiful landscape. It is a wonderful place to explore, or simply to sit and enjoy the peace and quiet. From its vantage point, the Garden offers a fantastic view of the city skyline featuring Edinburgh Castle.

The mission of RBGE is to explore, conserve and explain the world of plants for a better future.

We deliver world-leading plant science and conservation programmes to reduce the loss of global biodiversity and to achieve a greater understanding of plants, fungi and environmental sustainability.

We maintain and develop our internationally important collections in order to maximise their value as a research, education, conservation and heritage resource.

We provide learning and training in horticulture, plant science and biodiversity conservation to help people appreciate, understand and contribute to the conservation of plants and our natural environment.

We offer a first-class visitor attraction to enable more communities, families and individuals to enjoy and be inspired by our Garden and its facilities, to become more environmentally responsible and to support RBGE's work.

At the national level, as Scotland's botanical institute we play a significant role in delivering the Scottish Biodiversity Strategy,

All life is dependent on plants and fungi. Recent estimates indicate that 18–28 per cent of all flowering plant species have yet to be discovered and described and the fungal kingdom remains largely unexplored. In addition, any knowledge gaps for species already described often impede their conservation and sustainable use.

Our focus is on accelerating species discovery and the production of identification and knowledge resources. Knowledge of plants is crucial in understanding many of the challenges facing the world today, including climate change, the loss of biodiversity, food security, the development of new medicines and many more. Behind each new discovery in these fields is a plant that has a name, and behind each of those names is a herbarium specimen. Taxonomy – the science of classifying and naming the natural world – is at the heart of the work that is carried out by RBGE and this includes characterising species at imminent risk of extinction and those of greatest importance to humankind.

and as a non-departmental public body we give the Scottish Government access to scientific excellence and support the delivery of the Programme for Government. As a charity and an information hub working in many partnerships, RBGE is well placed to inspire a very wide audience to engage with the natural world that underpins our health, wealth and wellbeing, and to encourage people to discuss – and get involved with – current environmental issues.

At the international level we are a global resource, providing expertise, training and information to help people around the world conserve ecosystems and protect natural capital. Through our extensive partnerships, particularly in tropical South America, South East Asia, Nepal and the Sino-Himalaya and Middle East, we strengthen the global capacity to address the issues of plant conservation by undertaking joint projects and seeking and sharing examples of best practice. We have a strong focus on species-rich, economically important plant groups such as the gingers (Zingiberaceae), legumes (Leguminosae), begonias (Begoniaceae), conifers, African violets (Gesneriaceae) and the Sapotaceae.

Curcuma rhabdota

Streptocarpus cyaneus

Begonia brevirimosa

How the Garden grew

To trace the history of RBGE you can follow the trail back in time from Inverleith to Holyrood Park, where Scotland's first physic garden began in 1670 on a patch of ground no bigger than a tennis court. Walking through the busy city streets it is hard to imagine how much the world has changed in that time.

The Garden has its roots in a turbulent age. Scotland was impoverished by centuries of civil war and both Cromwell and the bubonic plague had left their mark on the capital city. Yet, almost incredibly, Edinburgh produced the skills, resources and determination to create one of Britain's first botanic gardens; only Oxford (1621) and Chelsea Physic Garden (1673) also date back to the 17th century.

At a time when it took six weeks to bring sugar from the West Indies, two adventurous Scottish doctors returned from a 'grand tour' of Europe determined to collect, grow and study plants for the treatment of disease. Robert Sibbald and Andrew Balfour, who met in France after travelling widely in Europe, leased their first plot near Holyrood Abbey with the help of local physicians prepared to pay for the cost of the "culture and importation of foreign plants".

Then, as now, botany was closely linked to horticulture. Sibbald and Balfour soon joined forces with James Sutherland, a skilful gardener and plant collector, who was

George Forrest

Robert Sibbald

hired in 1676 to care for around 900 plants at an annual salary of £20. In 1683, Sutherland produced his first catalogue (*Hortus Medicus Edinburgensis*) with a list of around 2,000 plants, including most of the herbs used in medicine at the time. By then, the Garden had moved to a bigger plot behind floodgates in the marshy Nor' Loch, now occupied by Platform 11 of Waverley Station. Sutherland retired in 1714 as the King's Botanist and the Botanic Garden's first Regius Keeper.

For much of the first 300 years of its existence, the Botanics, as it became known locally, grew by reaching out into the wider world. The Garden's development is closely linked to the Scottish Enlightenment and

> "I have given the English names as well as the Latin that the Catalogue might be the more useful to all persons and especially those unskilled in Latin."
>
> James Sutherland, 1683, Introduction to *A Catalogue of Plants in the Physical Garden at Edinburgh*, Part 1

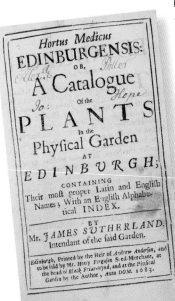

Hortus Medicus EDINBURGENSIS: OR, A Catalogue Of the PLANTS In the Physical Garden AT EDINBURGH; CONTAINING Their most proper Latin and English Names; With an English Alphabetical INDEX.

BY Mr. JAMES SUTHERLAND, Intendant of the said Garden.

Edinburgh, Printed by the Heir of Andrew Anderson, and to be sold by Mr. Henry Ferguson Seed-Merchant, at the head of Black Friar-Wynd, and at the Physical Garden by the Author, Anno DOM. 1683.

3

Edinburgh's great achievements in science and medicine (the relationship continues today with our world-renowned MSc in Biodiversity and Taxonomy of Plants, delivered jointly with the University of Edinburgh).

The collection of plants expanded with the British Empire as the Garden moved through the city. From the swampy Nor' Loch, the growing Schola Botanica moved to the better land and cleaner air of Leith Walk (now commemorated in Hopetoun Crescent Garden). The Leith Walk Garden included the Botanic Cottage (now newly rebuilt at Inverleith); the home of the principal gardener, it was also the main entrance to the Garden, and contained a classroom where every medical student was taught botany during the height of the Scottish Enlightenment. The final move to Inverleith in 1820 took three years and a lot of ingenuity to deliver the entire collection of plants, including mature trees, using transplanting machines invented by the Curator William McNab.

As the Garden grew – acquiring the grounds of Inverleith House for the Arboretum and former territory of the Caledonian Horticultural Society (later the RCHS) for the Rock Garden – so did the extraordinary wealth of plants collected by Scottish plant hunters in the 19th and early 20th centuries. In another

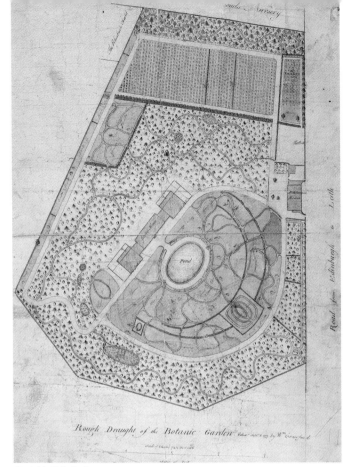

The Leith Walk Garden

A cypress tree (*Chamaecparis sp.*) being moved, 1894.

intriguing partnership between botanist and gardener, the plant hunter George Forrest introduced more than 10,000 specimens between 1905 and 1932 with the support of successive Regius Keepers, Isaac Bayley Balfour and William Wright Smith.

With the urban site bursting at the seams, RBGE grew during the 20th century, by exploiting Scotland's varied growing conditions. Benmore Botanic Garden in Argyll became part of RBGE in 1929, followed by Logan Botanic Garden in Dumfries & Galloway (1969) and finally Dawyck Botanic Garden in the Scottish Borders (1978).

Now, well into the 21st century, some of this rich collection is beginning its return journey. Plants grown from seed and cuttings in Edinburgh make their way back home to restore their native habitats while research continues across the world.

The Living Collection

RBGE is home to one of the world's richest collections of living plants, comprising over 128,000 individual plants and more than 13,500 species built up over centuries of global exploration, and is one of Scotland's National Collections. With the 3 million Herbarium specimens, and the Archive and Library collections, it forms the foundations of the Garden's research and educational programmes, and helps make RBGE one of the world's leading scientific botanic gardens.

The importance of correctly identifying and accurately naming plants for the purpose of prescribing them for medicinal use gave rise to the discipline we now call plant systematics. Although many different skills and technologies are now used, this still very much underpins botanic garden research. Plants cultivated in the Living Collection are used intensively to support research, and today this taxonomic research concentrates on understanding whole families and their genera, especially those that are species-rich yet poorly known and of economic or conservation importance. Samples from these plants are also used for DNA molecular and evolutionary development work.

Managing the Collection

Most of the new plant material cultivated in the Garden is of known wild origin, and has been collected mostly as seed but occasionally as live plants by Garden staff on field work in one of the 50 countries with which RBGE has collaborative links. Considerable value is added to this new plant material by the data that was collected: during fieldwork the knowledge gained through observing the plants in their native habitats is put to good use in ensuring that the plant is successfully propagated and then, when the appropriate time comes, planted in the correct location within the Garden.

Collecting Gesneriaceae in Tanzania

The future

No garden ever stands still – they are dynamic environments, changing hourly, daily and weekly – but as horticulturists our greatest challenge will probably be the impact of climate change. In recent years, in northern Britain we have experienced wetter than average late summers, autumn and winters, drier than average spring and early summers, two of the coldest winters in 30 years, a number of very mild winters and an increase in the frequency of severe wind events. We may have to change and adapt our horticultural techniques and practices to ensure the survival of the plants in our care.

RBGE's Living Collection is a legacy and testimony to the skill, dedication and hard work of generations of horticultural staff, students and volunteers. The plants and Garden landscapes are one of the foundations upon which RBGE's research, conservation, education, exhibitions and events are built. A walk through any of the four Gardens that comprise the

Living Collection is not only a stimulating and enjoyable feast for the senses but also a learning experience for anyone who has an interest in the natural environment.

Acer rubrum

Trees in the Garden

Visit any corner of the Garden and you will encounter magnificent and unusual trees. The presence of these trees creates much of the Garden's special atmosphere – the stately park grandeur of the lawns and the tranquillity and calm of the glades.

RBGE's tree collection stands as testament to the good husbandry and infinite enthusiasm of generations of horticulturists who have tended the Garden over the centuries. There are some magnificent specimens to discover as you explore.

The oldest trees in the collection have stood witness to the development of the Garden and predate its arrival at the site in Inverleith. A fine example of this is the venerable sweet chestnut (*Castanea sativa*) in the Rock Garden. Other highlights include the cedar of Lebanon (*Cedrus libani*), near the Glasshouses, which dates from 1826 and is one of the earliest trees to be planted by RBGE staff, and the extremely rare Catacol whitebeam (*Sorbus pseudomeinichii*), by the East Gate (only one wild specimen of this remains and can be found in a ravine in Glen Catacol on the isle of Arran).

Cedrus libani

Monkey puzzle tree (*Araucaria araucana*)   *Cedrus deodara*

In all, there are just over 3,500 trees in the Garden, comprising more than 730 species from 56 families. Around two-thirds are of known wild origin. This means we have records of where they were collected, in what habitat they were growing, who collected them and when. Many of these trees have been collected from habitats that have since been lost or have significantly reduced in size. Every tree has a story and every species has a niche in which it can exist in a natural ecosystem. Here in the city trees help make the urban environment liveable, improving air quality, buffering temperatures and noise, and keeping people in contact with nature.

A recent renaissance in plant collecting for the conservation of global plant diversity has seen many new trees grown from seed collected in the wild and grown on in our Nursery before being planted out in the Garden. RBGE is working to conserve many tree species both in cultivation and in natural habitats.

Weather plays a big role in what can be planted in the Garden. The increasingly frequent storms have seen the loss of many large specimens – and the survivors bear the scars.

Another threat is posed by the increasing array of introduced pests and pathogens, although the species richness and variation of age within the collection afford us some resilience to these threats.

Trees require specialist management and RBGE has a team of arborists who are responsible for managing and monitoring them, so that future generations can continue to enjoy what is among the finest collections in the world.

Demonstration Garden and Botanic Cottage

The Demonstration Garden is a vibrant and dynamic space dedicated to engaging people in hands-on food growing.

Edible Gardening Project and Polytunnel

Supported by players of People's Postcode Lottery, the Edible Gardening Project teaches the skills and knowledge people need to grow their own food. The crops are harvested and used for public events and community group cooking sessions, and to supply our onsite caterers. The teams look after much of the growing space in the Demonstration Garden, including the Polytunnel.

HND Beds

RBGE's students on the HND in Horticulture with Plantsmanship course are each assigned a plot, which they must plan, implement and evaluate.

Fruit Garden

The Fruit Garden demonstrates the best cultivars for domestic gardens in the East of Scotland climate. Many of the plants have been pruned into restricted forms, demonstrating how fruit can be grown in small spaces.

Schools

Several plots in the Demonstration Garden are looked after by local school groups. We work with a diverse range of schools, some with children with additional support needs.

Herbology

Founded as a physic garden in 1670, the Garden is steeped in the tradition of herbal medicine. Students from the RBGE Diploma in Herbology course look after the physic garden beds.

Botanic Cottage

The Botanic Cottage is the only surviving building of the 18th-century incarnation of RBGE that once stood on Leith Walk. It now holds the unique position of being simultaneously the newest and the oldest building in the Edinburgh Garden.

Designed by architects John Adam and James Craig, the Botanic Cottage was completed in 1765. Until 1821 it formed the centrepiece of RBGE on its former Leith Walk site where it

stood as the gateway to the Garden. The cottage also served as the Head Gardener's home and a classroom where Professor John Hope taught botany to medical students. It remains the oldest surviving classroom of the Scottish Enlightenment.

However, when RBGE moved to its present, much larger, site in Inverleith in the early 1820s, the Botanic Cottage was left behind. Over the next two centuries the cottage fell into a state of disrepair and was frequently vandalised. It was threatened with demolition in the early 2000s, before it was saved thanks to the tireless efforts of a community campaign. A new vision emerged: this historically significant building would be carefully dismantled stone-by-stone, moved across the city to the Edinburgh Garden's present site, and rebuilt. In keeping with its history as a place of learning, it would become a hub for a wide range of education and community activities, including exhibitions, performances and other events. The Cottage now has two teaching and community rooms, as well as two additional spaces in newly established wings on either side, opening up a wealth of opportunities for engagement that people of all ages and backgrounds can enjoy.

Queen Mother's Memorial Garden

Funded by the Queen Mother's Memorial Fund for Scotland, this Garden was established to reflect the Queen Mother's love of gardening.

Lachlan Stewart, an architect from the Highlands, was chosen to design the QMMG with the support of staff from RBGE, and was inspired by a Pictish cross found at Eassie, close to her home at Glamis.

The four corners of the Garden are planted to represent the 'four corners' of the world, to reflect the Queen Mother's love of travelling. The plants, selected for educational and ornamental purposes, are predominantly plants commonly found in cultivation, and are characteristic of the many geographical regions represented here. Scotland takes centre stage in the design, with a Celtic-style labyrinth planted with bog myrtle (*Myrica gale*) and extensive use of Caithness stone. Bog myrtle is a native of our wet uplands and evocative of the landscapes around the Castle of Mey.

The Memorial Pavilion is a tranquil shelter and a focal point for the Garden. The building materials were sourced locally, and great attention was paid to every detail in order to create a true celebration of Scotland's landscapes, wildlife and resources. The inside is decorated with shells collected by schoolchildren from around Scotland and the ceiling is lined with pine cones from RBGE's four Gardens.

The Garden was formally opened on 7 July 2006 by Her Majesty The Queen, accompanied by the Duke of Edinburgh and the Duke and Duchess of Rothesay.

Beech Hedge and Herbaceous Border

Every Garden has a feature that staff and visitors alike remember with affection, and at RBGE this is often the Beech Hedge. At a commanding height of 8m, it reaches along the full length of the 165m-long Herbaceous Border.

The history of the Beech Hedge is intertwined with that of the Herbaceous Border on its south side and the development of the Demonstration Garden to the north. The Herbaceous Border was created in 1902 by Regius Keeper Isaac Bailey Balfour and his Head Gardener Robert Lewis Harrow. This later included a hedge of 200 beech trees (*Fagus sylvatica*), which were purchased in 1906 at heights of 1–5ft (0.3–1.5m).

The area of land beyond the hedge was feued to the Garden in 1923 by the Fettes Trust. William Wright Smith, the Regius Keeper at the time, had a deep interest in forestry and timber supply, and the Garden worked closely with the newly created Forestry Commission, using this plot as a nursery to trial exotic conifer species.

Today there are a total of 158 individual trees in the hedge, and a close look through the foliage reveals the substantial girths of the trunks inside. The hedge is admired by visitors throughout the year. It is probably at its most attractive in spring, as the soft green of new growth gradually spreads throughout the length. It takes around 30 days for the whole hedge to change colour, starting in mid-April when the first dormant buds burst and cause the previous season's leaves to fall. Streaks of green appear along the hedge because during the time it takes the buds of the slowest plants to burst, others have already made up to 0.3m of extension growth.

The Beech Hedge is cut in early autumn each year, taking the current season's growth back to the previous season's framework of shoots.

The Herbaceous Border and the Beech Hedge.

Alpine House and Courtyard

Adapted to wild, high mountain tops, alpines are a real challenge to grow in the very different habitat of the maritime lowlands such as Edinburgh. As many cannot tolerate our wet Scottish climate, the traditional-style Alpine House was built in the 1970s to provide a dry environment for plants more used to spending winter beneath a protective blanket of snow. The plants are all grown in the traditional manner, in clay pots and plunged into sand, keeping the roots at an even cool temperature and level of moisture. Perfectly adapted to dry and windy conditions, alpines cannot tolerate any moisture on their foliage. A fan is used in the Alpine House to imitate the windy mountain conditions, and the plants are watered very carefully to ensure that no moisture reaches their foliage or flowers.

The Courtyard and Wall

Outside, in the Alpine Yard, a range of troughs are used to create individual landscapes representing miniature mountain tops. The wall retaining the Courtyard is one of the only limestone walls in the Garden and was built to accommodate plants that like more alkaline soil and enjoy a deep root run.

The Tufa House

This is the first building in a British botanic garden dedicated to growing and displaying alpine plants in the naturalistic surroundings of tufa, a type of soft rock. The tufa forms a natural rock face for the alpines to grow, and as a growing medium it improves the quality and survivability of these hard-to-grow plants, allowing them to grow slowly as they would in their native environment.

Alpines are particularly important to the scientific and conservation work of RBGE as they can be indicators of global warming-induced change, and the Tufa House complements the Traditional House by showcasing the latest techniques in the cultivation and care of alpines and showing how these techniques have evolved in the last 30 years.

The plants grown on the tufa wall are all cliff-dwellers in the wild, where their seed will blow into cracks and fissures in rock faces and become established. Outside, the tufa landscape is home to a range of outdoor alpines, with those requiring protection from the wet Scottish climate sheltering under the cantilevered canopy, making it possible to display plants that would normally only be grown in pots.

The Hot Wall

The wall backing the Alpine Courtyard is one of the few south-facing walls in the Garden, creating an opportunity for climbing plants from warmer climes to thrive alongside a 'hot border' of spiky shapes and brilliant colours. Particular highlights include the South African *Phygelius capensis* and *Agapanthus campanulatus* in the summer months. The pineapple broom (*Cytisus battandieri*), hailing from Morocco, produces sweetly scented yellow pineapple flowers atop its silvery foliage, while contrast is provided by the beautiful long-lasting blue 'thistle' flowers of *Eryngium giganteum*.

Temperate Palm House

The Temperate Palm House is without a doubt RBGE's most iconic building. It was built in 1858 as an extension to the Tropical Palm House and is the tallest traditional glasshouse in the UK and one of the tallest in the world.

Tropical Palm House

The Tropical Palm House was built in the early 1830s and is RBGE's oldest Glasshouse, made of heavy sandstone with a cast-iron and glass roof. The Bermudan fan palm (*Sabal bermudana*) was one of only two plants in the Glasshouses that were brought from the Leith Walk site in 1822.

Glasshouses and Glasshouse Borders

Victoria amazonica

Orchids and Cycads

The Orchids and Cycads House (below, left) brings together two opposite ends of the evolutionary scale: primitive cycads, which dominated the land flora some 65 million years ago, and a diverse range of orchids, the most sophisticated plants in the world. Orchids are the largest and most diverse family of flowering plants. The majority are epiphytic – they grow on trees. This makes them vulnerable when tropical rainforests are cleared to make way for oil palm or rubber tree plantations.

Plants and People

This is one of the hottest, most humid Glasshouses in the Garden, giving visitors a real sense of a tropical atmosphere. The space was designed around a pond filled to the brim in the summer with the giant waterlilies *Victoria amazonica*. The long light of Scotland's summers allows them to grow to their huge size and by June they will usually have produced a leaf over 2m wide that is able to support the weight of a small child. At first glance, the tropical plants in the Plants and People House may look unfamiliar, but the products made from them are an integral part of our daily lives – sugar, cocoa, rice and coffee plants are all grown here.

Ferns and Fossils

The cool shade of the Ferns and Fossils House (above, right) is welcome after the humid heat of the tropics. Here visitors can find a diverse range of ferns, from the architectural *Dicksonia* to the delicate feathery foliage of *Selaginella*. Conifers belong here too; like ferns, they are among the most ancient groups of plants, having been around for over 350 million years. Look out for *Acmopyle pancheri* – endemic to New Caledonia, it is now under threat as populations become fragmented by mining activities and fire. Among the living plants in this house are a number of carboniferous plant fossils; a large lump of coal that shows what a few million years of heat and compression can do to plant material in order to produce fossil fuels.

Calliandra haematocephala

Rainforest Riches

Enter this house and you will find yourself deep in the hot and humid atmosphere of the South American rainforest. In the real rainforest, much of the abundant plant life would be high above you, reaching for light in the canopy, but here it is down at ground level for you to admire. Featuring prominently are the bromeliads – a large family of over 2,000 species, of which the most familiar is the fragrant pineapple (*Ananas comusus*). Known as 'urn plants', their leaves spiral around a central hollow in a nest shape, storing water for the plant and creating a reservoir for other life forms, such as the tree frog. In late winter the bright red pompom flowers of the *Calliandra haematocephala* provide a splash of colour.

Temperate Lands

The plants in this house all originate from warm, temperate regions of the world. If you stand at the door of the lower section you will see two distinct planting zones. The first zone has plants from areas with hot summers. Many of these plants have hairy or thick leaves to protect them from water loss. The other zone contains plants from warm, moist evergreen forests, such as the Japanese blue oak (*Quercus glauca*) and the kauri (*Agathis australis*). Beneath these are many shade-loving plants such as begonias, hedychiums and ferns, which thrive in the dappled shade.

Arid Lands

The clear, dry air of the Arid Lands House transports you to the desert regions of the world, from the Americas to Africa and Arabia. The displays in this house explore the complex ecosystems of desert life; the plants are xerophytes, which have, over thousands of years, adapted in various ways to conserve water. In summer, the sandstone in the house absorbs the heat in the day and releases it at night when these areas can drop to freezing temperatures. The plants benefit from this heat, as well as from the shade that also helps with water conservation.

Montane Tropics

The Montane Tropics House represents the mountainous region of South East Asia from Borneo to Indonesia, which is home to the world's richest diversity and largest collection of *Vireya* rhododendrons. These beautiful plants can be found growing from sea level to over 4,000m in the wild yet are not frost hardy and need to be grown under glass. A case of carnivorous plants is another popular attraction in this house. These plants have adapted to grow in nutrient-poor soils by catching their own food. Look out for the cobra lily (*Darlingtonia californica*) and the Venus flytrap (*Dionaea muscipula*).

Strongylodon macrobotrys

Dionea muscipula

Amorphophallus titanum. The first recorded flowering in Scotland of the world's biggest and smelliest flower.

Glasshouse Borders

The Glasshouse Borders enjoy a microclimate that allows more tender plants to survive, thanks to the protection of the glass and the heat given off by the heating ducts. Behind the Glasshouses is the Chilean Terrace, showcasing many of the wild plants collected by RBGE staff, from the small *Calceolaria* to the *Berberis valdiviana* with its drooping racemes of saffron-yellow flowers.

Lowland (Wet) Tropics

Although covering the same geographical area as the Montane Tropics House, this environment represents the lowlands and so is warmer and wetter. The main feature of this house is a limestone cliff, providing the environment for members of the African violet family, the Gesneriaceae, within which are plants such as the goldfish plants (*Columnea*) and the lipstick vine (*Aeschynanthus*). Other members of the family are *Saintpaulia* and *Streptocarpus*, which are extremely important for studies in form evolution. Many of the species have not been cultivated before, and so knowledge of their requirements is critical to success here. Another key attraction is the large collection of gingers, the Zingiberaceae. Many species of this family have leaves that contain aromatic oils and the family includes culinary plants such as turmeric and cardamom as well as the familiar ginger *Zingiber officinale*.

Hiding around the back of the waterfall, a 1000-litre pot can be found, containing the tuber of the now-famous titan arum (*Amorphophallus titanum*), the world's biggest and smelliest flower.

Rhododendrons

RBGE has been the major centre for rhododendron studies since the late 19th century. Together, the collections in our four Gardens – Edinburgh, Benmore, Dawyck and Logan – comprise the world's richest assemblage of species rhododendrons. Around half of all the 1,000 known species are cultivated in the Gardens and include most of the temperate species and over one-third of those known in the tropics.

The *Rhododendron* collection currently comprises 657 species, 1,300 taxa, 3,984 accessions, 7,259 plant records and 10,869 plants. This collection would never even have been possible without the work of the intrepid plant collectors of the early 1900s who introduced many of the plants that are still in cultivation today. Isaac Bailey Balfour, Regius Keeper from 1888 until 1922, was instrumental in ensuring that plant hunter George Forrest was sent to China in 1904. It was perhaps this partnership and the new rhododendron material subsequently

Rhododendron 'Cynthia'

introduced by Forrest that would determine the direction the Herbarium and Garden would take over the next century. Since then, these introductions have been maintained through the vision and stewardship of generations of Garden staff.

The Edinburgh collection is planted largely according to subsections. This gives visitors a good visual impression of the different groups, and allows rhododendron specialists to locate and compare closely related plants easily.

Current and future challenges facing the cultivation of rhododendrons within the Living Collection include changes in rainfall patterns, temperature extremes and problems with pests and diseases.

Vireya rhododendrons

Around one-third of all rhododendrons, over 300 species, belong to the subgenus Vireya. These are principally montane plants growing at high altitudes in the South West Asian archipelago – from New Guinea in the east to the Philippines in the north and Sumatra in the north-west. Vireyas show a huge range of flower, colour, size and shape. *Rhododendron polyanthemum* from northern Sarawak has fragrant orange-red flowers pollinated by butterflies, while *Rhododendron loranthiflorum* is a scented, white-flowered species pollinated by moths.

Rhododendron polyanthemum

RBGE has the largest cultivated collection of Vireya rhododendrons in the world. As natives of the mountains of South East Asia, most like a cool, moist, frost-free environment. These plants thrive indoors in the Montane Tropics Glasshouse at the Edinburgh Garden, benefiting from the long hours of daylight and cool temperatures of the summer growing season in Scotland.

Rhododendron campanulatum 'Roland E. Cooper'

Rhododendron lemonara

Rhododendron loranthiflorum

RBGE Experimental Garden: research in action

The Experimental Garden, situated near the East Gate, uses Scottish native plants and innovative interpretation, art and way-marking to guide visitors through a garden inspired by science.

The Garden contains a number of experimental plots that are monitored by research scientists. These aim to introduce the science that occurs behind the scenes at the RBGE, and more generally across research institutes across Edinburgh, to our garden visitors.

This area centres on a marked trail through Scottish native woodland. The naturalistic planting features prominent stands of avens (*Geum*) and campion (*Silene*), as well as a large feature planting of foxgloves (*Digitalis*). Each of these areas tell a story about an area of current research. Other highlights include the large pond and ruined bothy.

Initial work on this area started in 2015, with major redevelopment starting in 2017.

Silene latifolia

Foxglove *Digitalis purpurea*

Exhibitions and Events

An important aspect of RBGE's work is furthering our appreciation and understanding of the natural world through a programme of public and community engagement. Details of all our events and courses are available online or at the John Hope Gateway.

The Garden and its buildings are wonderful venues for exhibitions and provide a global setting for cultural engagement; bringing together plants, science and the arts. This includes exhibitions by leading botanical and contemporary artists, craft and design shows, and a wide range of events including outdoor theatre, film and music.

Sitting in the centre of the garden is Inverleith House – a fine Georgian mansion that was built in 1774 as a private home and was acquired by RBGE in 1875. Inverleith House and the John Hope Gateway provide the primary indoor venues for exhibitions. Out in the Gardens there is a small collection of permanent sculptures, and the glasshouses are also occasionally used to display art inspired by nature, set in the exquisite and exotic collection of plants from the warmer regions of the world.

Rock Garden

Climb to the viewpoint at the highest point of the Garden and you will be rewarded with views over the Rock Garden and of the city of Edinburgh's spectacular skyline, a stunning backdrop to the collection of over 5,000 plants from the world's mountains as well as Arctic and rocky Mediterranean habitats.

The Rock Garden was first created in 1870 by Curator James McNab in order to accommodate the Garden's growing alpine collection. He used the stone from the wall that once separated the Experimental Garden from the neighbouring Botanic Garden and architectural salvage from the city's buildings.

The original Rock Garden was typical of Victorian-era design and consisted of over 2,000 small compartments separated by stone boundaries. Between 1907 and 1914 it was completely redesigned to create a more natural style of landscape, with the scree area on the southern side added in the 1920s.

The alpine collection expanded rapidly as plant collectors returned from their travels and the Rock Garden now displays approximately 5,000 species from the great mountain ranges of the world, in particular large concentrations of plants from Chile, China, Europe, Japan, North America and South Africa.

Alongside the true alpine species are many small woody plants and bulbous species that complement the landscape. There is a range of small conifer species which are suited to cultivation here as well as many dwarf conifer cultivars.

The western side of the Rock Garden that borders the Woodland Garden is where many dwarf rhododendron species are planted, allowing a smooth transition between the landscapes. These are complemented by the primula, meconopsis and lily species interspersed among them.

Among the highlights are colourful spring flowering bulbs including daffodils, snowdrops and crocuses. Late spring and early summer sees the peak flowering of the dwarf

A man and boy enjoying the view in the Victorian Rock Garden in around 1894.

rhododendrons and alpines throughout the area. At this time the true high alpines are at their best, from the beautiful European *Pulsatilla* to the North American *Penstemon*. Autumn highlights include the flowering of the numerous *Colchicum* species and the needles of *Pinus sylvestris* 'Aurea' turning from green to golden-yellow.

Several beds in the Rock Garden contain plants of a particular geographical origin. These include the New Zealand bed, and the East Valley where species from Japan and the Himalayas are concentrated. Recent additions to the Rock Garden include the Scottish Native bed, which borders the Scottish Heath Garden on the eastern boundary and showcases our rare and threatened plants from several typical habitat types from sea level to high alpines. These are complemented by some more common associated species from the various habitats growing alongside them.

Primula denticulata

Iris japonica

Woodland Garden

You can feel the atmosphere change as you enter the Woodland Garden. It is cooler and quieter here in the shelter of the canopy, and the pine-scented air is moist and still.

The Woodland Garden was extensively developed in the 1930s and 1940s, with large conifers planted to create a suitable microclimate for the rhododendrons and other woodland plants that were being introduced from the Himalayas and China. Many such species would not normally survive in Edinburgh's dry, sunny climate and so horticultural staff members have recreated the natural conditions in which these plants would grow. This tranquil area is today divided into the Upper and Lower Woodland Garden.

Upper Woodland Garden

This area is home to some magnificent trees, including the coastal redwoods (*Sequoia sempervirens*) – among the world's tallest tree species. A circle of *Sequoiadendron giganteum* (giant redwoods) creates a cathedral-like atmosphere, making this a popular location for outdoor weddings and other ceremonies. These redwoods, planted in the 1920s, have now reached over 24m in height. In 1990, the grove was renamed the John Muir Grove, honouring the Scots-born writer, explorer and conservationist who founded the US National Park system.

Other trees of note include many endangered conifers from around the world. Unusual rowan and birch add to the autumn colour with their fruits and turning leaves, and sit alongside beautiful magnolia species from Asia and North America that flower in the spring.

Understory plantings of large-leaved rhododendron species and choice woodland herbaceous plants thrive in the microclimate created by the canopy. Some of the older rhododendrons were collected by the pioneering plant collectors of the early 20th century.

Among the other highlights are the spectacular giant Himalayan lily (*Cardiocrinum giganteum*) that flowers in the early summer and goes on to produce architectural seed heads, which persist throughout the winter. Choice collections of herbaceous plants include a large collection of North American trillium species, meconopsis (Himalayan poppies), alongside many other beautiful species from Asia and Europe, including hosta, lily and primula species.

The Peat Walls in the Lower Woodland Garden

Lower Woodland Garden

The Lower Woodland Garden includes the terraced Peat Walls, where a cool, damp, shady habitat allows the cultivation of many choice species. Constructed in 1939, they were based on an idea pioneered at Logan Botanic Garden a decade earlier.

The area is terraced with oak logs, pine root plates and blocks of peat, creating the perfect habitat for dwarf ericaceous shrubs, beautiful autumn-flowering gentian species and drifts of primula species from the Himalayas.

Highlights of the area are the dwarf rhododendron species flowering in spring alongside delicate erythroniums and primulas. Autumn sees colour return to the area with the fabulous turning leaves of the shrubs and the blue-flowered gentians carpeting the ground. A collection of rarely cultivated plants from Asia, Europe and North America ensures year-round interest.

Meconopsis (Himalayan blue poppies)

Cardiocrinum giganteum

Primula viali

Gentiana ternifolia

Chinese Hillside

In China there are about 32,000 species of native plants, accounting for around one in eight of the world's plant species. Half of these occur in Yunnan Province, in the south-west of the country. China's rich flora remained unknown in Europe until around 150 years ago, when plant collectors such as George Forrest began to explore the world, returning with thousands of plant specimens. Forrest made seven trips to Yunnan between 1904 and 1932, and the seeds he brought back changed the face of British gardens, introducing the now familiar rhododendrons, primula, camellia and many more for the first time.

Now, because of deforestation, human urbanisation and pollution, plant and animal species are in need of urgent conservation in Yunnan. RBGE has a long-term commitment to the conservation of this area, working closely with local communities who depend on the plants for food, shelter

and medicine. It enjoys an especially close relationship with Kunming Institute of Botany, with which it is twinned. This commitment was consolidated with the creation of the Lijiang Botanic Garden and Jade Dragon Field Station, opened in 2002 and declared the UK's first joint scientific laboratory in China. In addition, RBGE was a contributor to the first English written Flora of China, a landmark foundation for reference and future taxonomic work.

The Chinese Hillside highlights RBGE's well-established links with China and its outstanding collection of Chinese plants. Formally opened in 1997, this part of the Garden recreates for visitors the experience of climbing a hillside in Yunnan. It includes winding paths, a waterfall and a T'ing, or traditional small pavilion, and features around 16,000 plants collected from Yunnan, many rare and endangered. The planting follows the ecological course of a hillside in the wild, with different plants at different altitudes. The plants, which include a range of beautiful rhododendrons, as well as various species of *Cotoneaster* and *Sorbus*, have largely been allowed to drift through the site and grow together in a natural way.

Rhododendron: The Oriental ornamental

The Garden through the seasons

Late winter to spring

The Alpine House provides some real gems during late winter and it is here that the first flowers of the year will burst into life. Nearby, witch hazels (*Hamamelis mollis* from China and *Hamamelis japonica* from Japan) produce their lemon-peel flowers and perfume the mild days with an intense scent. Spring seems to come a little earlier each year. Snowdrops (*Galanthus nivalis* and other species) form a carpet below the trees from early January.

Hamamelis mollis

Magnolia kobus

Trilium chloropetalum

Late spring to early summer

In late spring the Japanese magnolia (*Magnolia kobus*) blooms throughout the Garden and the related *Michelia figo* in the Temperate Palm House fills the air with its exotic perfume. Visitors to the Garden in spring and early summer cannot miss the rhododendron collection, from the dwarf alpine species in the Rock Garden to the larger species growing in the Woodland Garden and Copse.

Wake robbins (trilliums) bloom in abundance throughout the Woodland Garden, Peat Walls and Copse – look for *Trillium grandiflorum* and *Trillium chloropetalum*. And in many parts of the Garden, hellebores make a welcome appearance.

Rosa 'Golden Jubilee'

Meconopsis 'Slieve Donard'

Summer

Now you are spoilt for choice. The Herbaceous Border is a spectacular sight in the height of summer. The striking Rosa 'Golden Jubilee' can be found in the Queen Mother's Memorial Garden, while the many bulbs of *Cardiocrinum giganteum* throw up statuesque flower spikes every five to seven years to ensure that there will be a fine display in early summer. Swathes of blue poppies (*Meconopsis betonicifolia*) enjoy the cool shade of the woodland while *Sutherlandia frutescens* from southern Africa displays its striking red flowers at the Alpine House.

Autumn

Next year's buds are already on the trees but you will see them only if a sudden gale has blown the blazing autumn colour to the ground. The scarlet apples on *Malus pumila* 'Dartmouth' are a taste of the many vibrantly coloured fruits to be found on the Chinese Hillside – roses, *Pyracantha*, *Malus* and *Sorbus* abound. Brilliant pink *Nerine bowdenii* enjoys the autumn sun by the Glasshouses, while *Schizostylus coccinea* cultivars display their flowers among the seed heads in the Rock Garden. Flowers of colchicums, the autumn crocus, make a brief but exuberant appearance around the Garden and many smaller species can be seen in the Alpine House. *Cercidiphyllum japonicum* fills the air with the smell of burnt sugar by the Pond lawns and elsewhere in the Garden.

Winter

Bare branches trace patterns against the winter sky but even this season brings colour, perfume and birdlife. Vibrant red and green stems of *Cornus stolonifera* 'Flaviramea' and *Salix alba* 'Britzensis' glow in the clear northern light. The Herbaceous Border is a favourite for seed-eating birds, and seed heads glisten in the early sun of a frosty morning. On the coldest days, it is always summer in the Glasshouses, where you can breathe in the warm fragrances of faraway places. But outside, on the Birch Lawn, pale yellow catkins of *Corylus avellana* are a hint that spring is on its way.

Herbarium and Library

In addition to the Living Collection, RBGE houses two other National Collections – the Herbarium and the Library.

The Herbarium houses a collection of more than 3 million plant specimens, with 10,000–30,000 new items preserved each year. The Library is Scotland's National Collection of botanical and horticultural literature and contains more than 70,000 books, the earliest of which dates back to the 15th century, as well as large collections of original artworks, manuscripts, photographs and other archival materials. The Library is open to the public.

What is a herbarium?

A herbarium is a collection of dried plants that are arranged in a systematic order. A small plant or a part of a larger plant is pressed flat, dried and mounted on a piece of archival card known as a herbarium sheet, accompanied by a label containing information on where, when and by whom the plant was collected. The RBGE Herbarium serves as a reference library for plant life: when a new species is discovered the name is associated with a herbarium specimen (the 'type specimen') that defines the characteristics of that species.

Working collections

The RBGE Herbarium and Library Collections contain many wonderful historical objects, but they are different from many museum collections in that all these objects are all part of working collections. They provide a unique research facility that is used both by scientists based at the Garden and researchers from around the world in order to explore, conserve and explain the world of plants.

The collections enable researchers to compare the biodiversity of certain areas over long periods of time and thus provide invaluable information on change. They are also important as sources of information about the social and economic conditions in which RBGE people have worked throughout its history. Plant collectors such as George Forrest and Joseph Rock were often the first people from the western world to visit strange and exotic lands and their diaries and collecting books provide a unique insight into life in these countries at those points in time.

Royal
Botanic Garden
Edinburgh

Text © Royal Botanic Garden Edinburgh, 2017

ISBN: 978-1-910877-09-8

Images by Peter Clarke, Alan Pottinger, Brenda White,
Lynsey Wilson and Robert Unwin

Text by Anna Stevenson

Design/layout by Caroline Muir

The Royal Botanic Garden Edinburgh (RBGE) is supported by the Scottish Government's
Rural and Environmental Science and Analytical Services Division.
The Royal Botanic Garden Edinburgh is a Charity registered in Scotland (number SC007983).

All information correct at time of going to press.

Printed by Potts Print (UK) Ltd

FSC
www.fsc.org
MIX
Paper from
responsible sources
FSC® C019788